A *Doonesbury* book

The President Is a Lot Smarter Than You Think

by G.B. Trudeau

POPULAR LIBRARY • NEW YORK

Introduction

by Art Buchwald

I have been asked to write a short introduction to Garry Trudeau's book featuring the best of his cartoons. I have agreed to do this for several reasons. One is that I am a great admirer of Mr. Trudeau's syndicated strip "Doonesbury," and secondly, I am very envious of him.

The difference between a cartoonist and a columnist is that a cartoonist can parlay his work into so many other financially rewarding fields. I suspect that in the very near future we will be seeing Doonesbury Sweatshirts, B.D. Star Quarterback Football Games, Megaphone Mark Campus Radical Ashtrays, and God knows how many boxes of Hallmark "Calvin" greeting cards.

If Trudeau follows the pattern of other successful cartoonists, he will have to incorporate himself, just to handle the television and movie rights of the strip. We can also look forward to a large amusement park on the Yale campus called "Doonesburyland."

In the not too distant future he will be the second richest man I know. The first is Charles Schultz, who draws "Peanuts."

I figure if I write an introduction to Trudeau's book, he may give me a chance to get in on some of the action. Five percent of Trudeau ten years from now will solve all my retirement problems.

I am not a believer in introductions for cartoonists' books. I think cartoons should speak for themselves.

Trudeau's characters speak as well for themselves as any appearing on the comic pages of our newspapers today.

As with all anti-Establishment figures, Mr. Trudeau will soon be an honored member of the Establishment, if he is not already. But the reader should not despair. He didn't sell out—he just sold well.

I wish him luck in all his future endeavors. I have already found a great location for a "Doonesbury Hamburger Heaven" near the White House, and when Garry starts handing out franchises, I hope he keeps me in mind.

Washington, D. C.

December, 1971

Dear Michael,
You'll be happy
to hear I am
working hard.

This is because
I want to go
to college after
all.

LOOK OUT
FOR THE
BRICKS.

Dear Mr. President;
I am writing in protest of my father being laid off at work. He only stays alive by being a janitor nights.

Last spring you said there is just as much dignity in being a janitor as in being President of the United States.

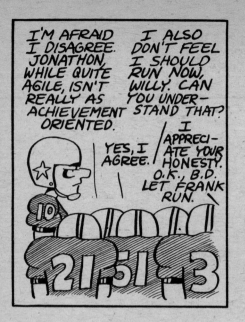